To my daughters. KJ, GJ, VJ, EJ, JJ.
You are a force to be reckoned with.

www.mascotbooks.com

Maddie Makes Moves

For more information, please contact:
Mascot Books
620 Herndon Parkway, Suite 320
Herndon, VA 20170
info@mascotbooks.com

Library of Congress Control Number: 2020905820

CPSIA Code: PRTWP0720A
ISBN-13: 978-1-64543-373-6

Printed in South Korea

Maddie Makes Moves

Anne Jeudy

Illustrated by
Jenny Phelps

"This is impossible!" yells Maddie.

Maddie plays soccer with her sister and her friends at the park.

"You just have to jump higher, kick farther, and be tougher!" says Maddie's older sister Macy. She is a *lot* better at soccer.

"How am I supposed to do that?" asks Maddie. She starts to walk around the park.

"How will I jump higher? How will I kick farther? How will I be tougher?"

Maddie has an idea.

She walks to the pond and leans her head close to the water.

Maddie yells, "I need a frog to teach me how to jump higher!"

Two tiny eyes pop out of the water.

Maddie says, "I need your help. I want to learn how to really jump."

"I can help you jump higher," says the frog. "But after I teach you, will you teach someone else? I want the world to do frog hops!"

"Frog hops!" says Maddie. "Can you show me how to do frog hops?"

"Try this with me," he says.

They do frog
hops together
and count:

"1-2-3-4-5"

After they finish the frog hops,
Maddie's legs are tired.

"Practice these frog hops,
and you will jump higher," says the frog.

"Thank you!" says Maddie.

"The frog showed me how to jump higher," Maddie says, "but how will I kick farther? Every time I kick, I lose my balance and fall over."

Maddie has another idea.

Maddie yells, "I need a bird to teach me balance!"

A bluebird peeks out from behind a leaf.

"I need your help," Maddie says. "I want to balance so I can kick farther without falling."

"I can help you balance," says the bluebird. "But after I teach you, will you teach someone else? I want the world to do flying birds."

"Flying birds!" says Maddie. "Can you show me how to do flying birds?"

The bluebird
stands on
one leg.

She leans
forward...

and slowly
flaps her
wings.

"Try this with me,"
says the bluebird.
They do flying birds and count:

"1-2-3-4-5"

"Don't forget to stand on your other leg,"
says the bluebird. Maddie switches legs and they count:

"6-7-8-9-10"

When they finish the flying birds,
Maddie loses her balance and falls.

"Practice these flying birds and you will have
better balance to kick the ball," says the bluebird.

"High five!" says Maddie.

"The frog showed me how to jump and the bluebird showed me how to balance, but how will I become tougher?"

Maddie has another idea.

Maddie thinks of the biggest, toughest animal there is.

Maddie yells into the forest, "I need a bear to teach me how to be tough!"

Maddie hears leaves crunching and twigs breaking.

A big brown bear strolls out from behind a berry bush.

"I need your help," says Maddie.
"I want to learn how to be tough like a bear."

"I can help you be tough," says the bear.
"But after I teach you, will you teach someone else?
I want the world to do bear crawls."

"Bear crawls!" yells Maddie.
"Can you show me how to do bear crawls?"

The bear gets down on his four paws.

He crawls low to the ground.

"Try this with me," says the bear. "And don't forget to growl."

They do bear crawls and growl:

"1-2-3-4-5"

When Maddie says "5," the bear collapses with a thud. "What a workout!" he says.

Maddie and the bear both laugh. Maddie tells the bear, "Practice these more and you will be tougher!"

"Maddie!" Macy yells. "What are you doing out here? Soccer takes practice and you can't give up."

"I didn't give up, Macy," says Maddie. "I was just out here...exercising!"

Maddie runs on the field and does everything the animals showed her.

"How did you get so much better at soccer?" asks Macy.

Glossary of Exercises

Try these exercises for 5-10 repetitions and 3 sets each!

Repetition: One complete movement of an exercise

Set: A group of consecutive repetitions

Example: *I did 2 sets of 10 repetitions of push-ups.*

This means you did 10 consecutive push-ups,
rested, and did another 10 push-ups.

Frog hops: Stand with your feet wide and your toes pointed forward. Bend your knees like you're about to sit in a chair, then jump straight up. Land like you started, on your toes with bent knees and feet wide.

Flying birds: Stand on one leg, with your knee slightly bent. Raise your other leg straight behind you. Send your arms out wide like a bird about to take flight, keep your belly button in, and slowly flap your arms like wings. Switch to the opposite leg and repeat the exercise.

Bear crawls: Start on your hands and knees, with hands shoulder-width apart and knees hip-width apart on the ground. Staying low to the ground, dig in with your toes to lift your knees so that only your hands and feet are on the ground. Now that you're in bear crawl position, look forward and crawl with your right hand and your left foot, followed by your left hand and right foot.

Anne Jeudy is a mother of five daughters and currently lives in Forsyth County, Georgia. She is a lifelong athlete, from growing up skiing in northern New Hampshire, where she was born and raised, and playing soccer, field hockey, and softball; to now being an avid weightlifter, certified personal trainer, preschool teacher, and soccer coach. Her inspiration for *Maddie Makes Moves* comes from her love of women in sports and encouraging her own daughters to be brave and never give up. Anne plays the trombone, is a member of the Society of Children's Book Writers and Illustrators, and has a degree in English from the University of New Hampshire.